Help Your Child To Read

Silly Sheep

G000256144

ALLAN AHLBERG and ERIC HILL

GRANADA
London Toronto Sydney New York

Help Your Child To Read

Parents <u>can</u> help their children to start reading. It is not difficult, nor is it necessary to be a trained teacher. In many ways home is a better place to start than school. In school your child will share the teacher's time with 25 or 30 others. At home he can have your undivided attention.

The series HELP YOUR CHILD TO READ is a set of books for parents to <u>share</u> with their children. The books contain stories, rhymes and games. Also, on page 3 of each book, there are practical suggestions for parents: ways in which they can help their children to start reading.

Writing and Reading

Writing and reading go together, just like talking and listening. Your child will make more sense of reading, when he understands that print is talk written down.

So, let him see written language round the house: notices, letters, shopping lists. Get him a mug with his name on it. Label some of his things with his name. Offer to write titles for his pictures. Above all, get a blackboard. Write messages to him ('Today we are going swimming') and for him ('Welcome home, dad!').

To see his own words written down and then read them back, is a great help to a child. So, if you want to help yours, become a secretary for a while.

Meet Silly Sheep

When Silly Sheep
goes out to play
he puts on
all his clothes
his wellingtons
in case it rains
his coat
in case it blows
his swimming trunks
in case it shines
his gloves
in case it snows.

The only trouble is
with all these clothes
and more
poor Silly Sheep
can't run and play
he can't get through
the door!

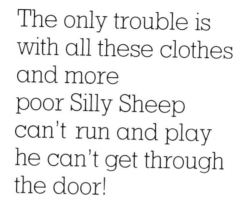

If I had wings said Silly Sheep

I could fly.

If I had wheels

I could
roll down the road.

TOWN

If I were twins

I could
play hide-and-seek
with myself.

If I were a giant

I'd need
a bigger house.

If I had
bread-and-butter

I could
make a jam sandwich —
if I had jam.

If I were
big and grey
and had a trunk —

ZOO

Counting sheep

How many baby sheep?
How many black sheep?
How many sheep
with hats on?
How many sheep
with glasses on?
How many sheep
with scarves
and gloves
and woolly jumpers on?

How many sheep
with a potted plant on?

Silly Sheep's poem

Hey diddle diddle
pig in the middle
the frog rode
into a tree.

Silly Sheep laughed
to see such fun
and the bear ran away
with his tea!

Every time I say something, you say— just like me!

Yes!

I went up one step —
just like me!
I went up two steps —
just like me!
I went up three steps —
just like me!
I opened the door —
just like me!
Looked out of the window —
just like me!

Just like ... me?

And saw a monkey —
just like . . . me!

Goodnight Silly Sheep

Silly Sheep
has gone to bed
his clothes
are in a heap.

He meant to rest
his woolly head
but his feet
have gone to sleep.

The end